Usborne
Little Book of
Easter Activities

Rebecca Gilpin and Fiona Watt
Recipes by Catherine Atkinson
Additional ideas by Ray Gibson

Designed and illustrated by Non Figg,
Molly Sage, Andrea Slane, Sarah Sherley-Price,
Jo Webb, Amanda Barlow, Chris Chaisty,
Michaela Kennard and Nelupa Hussain

Photographs by Howard Allman
Additional photography: Ray Moller

American editor: Carrie Armstrong

Contents

Pecking hens and chicks   4
Bunny wrapping paper   6
Field of rabbits   8
A chick card   10
Sheep and lambs picture   12
A chick puppet   14
Rabbit face   16
Potato-printed chicks   18
Giant spring flower prints   20
Bunny napkin rings   22
Surprise eggs   24
A bunch of daffodils   26
Easter flowerpots   28
Chicken and egg card   30
Cress egg-heads   32

Easter recipes

Chirpy chick cupcakes	34
Flower candy	36
Sticky Easter muffins	38
Sunshine toast	40
Easter truffles	42
Marzipan animals and eggs	44
Easter fudge	46
Colored eggs	48
Easter cake	50
Chocolate nests	52
Easter fruit bread	54
Spiced Easter cookies	56
Easter daisy cookies	58
Cheesy chicks	60
Boxes and bags	62
Easter tags	64

Pecking hens and chicks

1. Fold a paper plate in half. Open it out, then paint the back of the plate like this.

2. Fold the plate in half again. For a beak, cut a triangle from paper and glue it onto the corner.

3. Cut some triangles from brightly-colored paper. These will be the spikes on top of the hen's head.

Cut feather shapes from paper and glue them on.

For a chick, instead of using a paper plate, cut around a saucer on stiff paper. Don't add the spikes to the head.

Tape the tail onto the
back of the plate.

4. Glue the spikes to the
back of the plate. Cut
out circles of paper and
glue them on for eyes.

5. Cut lots of thin strips of
brightly-colored tissue
paper. Make the strips
as long as your hand.

6. Gather the strips into
a bunch and twist them
together at one end.
Tape them on for a tail.

Rock the hens and
chicks to make
them peck.

Bunny wrapping paper

Use a wax crayon.

1. Crayon lots of heads on a large piece of paper. Space them out.

2. Add two ears to each head. Draw lines inside the ears, too.

3. Use the same crayon to draw a fat body below each head.

4. Draw two feet below the bunny's body, and a wavy line for a tail.

5. Add two eyes, a nose and a curved mouth to each bunny.

6. Add whiskers. Then, fill in the bunnies with felt-tip pens.

Wrap Easter presents in your decorated paper.

You could try drawing a bunny like this, too.

6

For a gift tag, draw a bunny, then cut around it and glue it onto a piece of stiff paper. For more gift tags, see page 64.

Field of rabbits

1. Press your hand into yellow paint, then press it all over a piece of paper. Add green on top.

Paint the rabbit on top of the background.

2. When the paint is dry, dip a finger into some paint and finger paint a fat shape.

3. For a head, dip your fingertip in the paint and rub it around and around in a circle.

4. Dip a finger into the paint again and add ears. Add four legs on the rabbit's body.

5. Dip a fingertip into white paint and add a tail. Add tiny dots for eyes, too.

6. When the paint is dry, use a felt-tip pen to add a nose, whiskers and a dot in each eye.

You could use your fingertips to print flowers around the rabbits.

A chick card

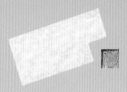

1. Cut the corner off an old envelope. Crayon all over one side of it, and inside, too.

2. Fold a piece of stiff paper in half. Crease the fold well, then open it out again.

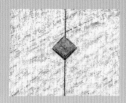

3. Glue the corner of the envelope in the middle of the card. This makes the beak.

4. Lift the top of the beak. Close the card and rub across it to flatten the beak.

5. Open the card. Draw a chick around the beak. Add some eyes, legs and feet.

You could cut out half an egg shape and glue it on below your chick.

Paint streaks across some paper with a big brush. Glue on a beak when the paint is dry.

6. Draw flowers around the chick, or cut them out from bright paper and glue them on.

For a long card, glue body shapes over the fold, then add the beaks.

Try gluing on little pieces of tissue paper for a body.

11

Sheep and lambs picture

You don't need to wind it neatly.

1. For the bodies, draw big and little wavy shapes, like these, on pieces of thin paper. Then, cut them out.

2. Dip the shapes into water. Shake off the drops, then arrange them on a large piece of paper.

3. Tape the end of some wool or yarn onto an old birthday card or postcard. Wind the yarn around and around.

Make sure both pieces of tape are on the same side.

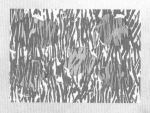

4. When the card is covered, cut off any leftover yarn. Secure the end of the yarn with a piece of tape.

5. Paint the yarn green on the side without the tape. Press it all over the paper. Add more paint as you go.

6. Gently peel off the paper bodies. When the paint is dry, add faces and legs with paint or a thick felt-tip pen.

Use a fingertip to print flowers in the grass.

A chick puppet

1. Fold three paper plates in half. Then, fold each one back the other way, along each fold.

You don't need these pieces.

2. Cut one of the plates in half along its fold. Cut a strip from the edge of one half.

Try rolling two different shades of crêpe paper together, then cut the slits (see step 7).

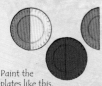

Paint the plates like this.

3. Mix some household (PVA) glue with yellow, red and orange paints. Paint the plates.

4. When the paint is dry, fold the two whole plates and put them together, like this.

5. Carefully join the orange and red parts together with lots of small pieces of tape.

6. Turn the plates over and tape the smaller orange piece of plate onto the red half.

7. Cut a strip of crêpe paper as long as your hand. Roll it tightly, then cut lots of slits.

8. Tape the crêpe paper roll to the back of the yellow part. Tape it on near the top.

9. Cut eyes from paper and glue them on. Cut middles for the eyes and glue them on, too.

10. Cut a hole in a sock. Put your hand into the sock and push your thumb through the hole.

11. Put your hand into the bird, like this. Open and close your hand to make the bird talk.

Rabbit face

To make rabbit "ears", tie your hair in bunches and use hair gel to make them stand up.

1. Rub a damp sponge into some lilac face paint. Rub it lightly around and around.

2. Dab the sponge onto one cheek and twist it a little. Lift your hand and dab it on again.

Put on a matching T-shirt before you paint your face.

If you don't have lilac face paint, you can mix other paints to make it (see below).

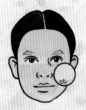

3. Dab the face paint over the cheeks, nose and chin. Leave a bare patch around the mouth.

4. Continue dabbing paint onto the forehead, leaving bare patches around the eyes.

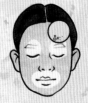

5. With closed eyes and mouth, dab white face paint onto the bare patches.

6. Sponge darker lilac on the cheeks and forehead. Brush on pink eyebrows.

7. Dip the brush in the pink face paint again and paint the tip of the nose, like this.

8. Paint a line from the nose to the top lip. Fill in the bottom lip. Add dots, whiskers and teeth.

Mixing paints

If you don't have lilac face paint, you can make it by mixing together red, white and blue paints.

Mix them to make purple.

1. Dab red face paint on the back of your hand. Add some blue.

2. Clean your sponge then dab on a little white to make lilac.

Potato-printed chicks

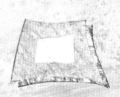

1. Lay several kitchen paper towels onto a thick pile of old newspapers.

2. Pour some bright yellow paint on top. Spread the paint with the back of a spoon.

3. Cut a potato in half. Then, cut away the two sides, like this, to make a handle.

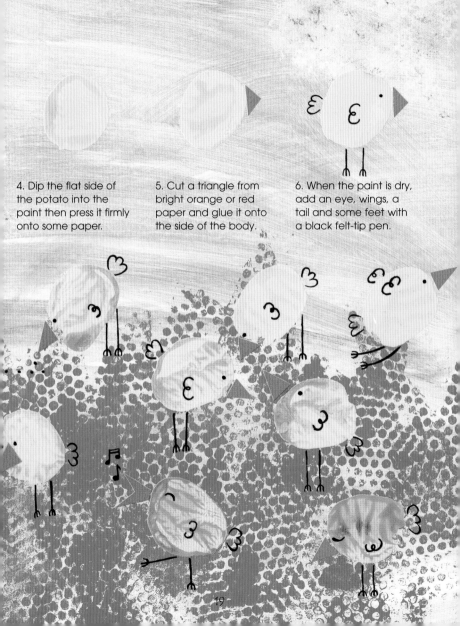

4. Dip the flat side of the potato into the paint then press it firmly onto some paper.

5. Cut a triangle from bright orange or red paper and glue it onto the side of the body.

6. When the paint is dry, add an eye, wings, a tail and some feet with a black felt-tip pen.

Giant spring flower prints

Primroses

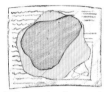

1. Spread yellow paint onto a newspaper. Cut a small, hard pear in half and press it into the paint.

2. Press the pear onto some paper, then lift it off. Put a bottle top at the pointed end of the shape you have printed.

3. Print more pear shapes around the bottle top. Dip the pear in the paint each time you do a print.

4. Lift off the bottle top. Then, dip a fingertip into green paint. Print dots in the middle of the pear prints.

5. For big leaves, cut a large potato in half. Dip it in green paint and press it onto the paper, around the flower.

The prints on these pages are much smaller than the ones you will do.

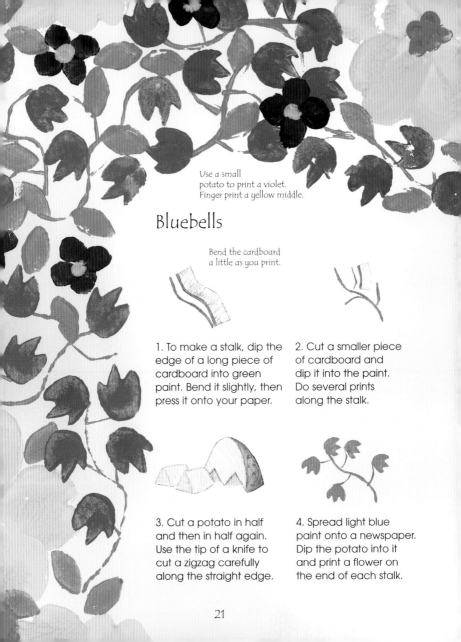

Use a small
potato to print a violet.
Finger print a yellow middle.

Bluebells

Bend the cardboard
a little as you print.

1. To make a stalk, dip the edge of a long piece of cardboard into green paint. Bend it slightly, then press it onto your paper.

2. Cut a smaller piece of cardboard and dip it into the paint. Do several prints along the stalk.

3. Cut a potato in half and then in half again. Use the tip of a knife to cut a zigzag carefully along the straight edge.

4. Spread light blue paint onto a newspaper. Dip the potato into it and print a flower on the end of each stalk.

Bunny napkin rings

1. Take a piece of stiff paper the length of your hand and fold it in half. Draw half the shape of a bunny's head, like this.

2. Carefully cut around the shape of the head. Then, open out the paper and use felt-tip pens to draw a face.

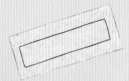

3. For the bunny's body, draw a rectangle on a piece of stiff paper twice the length of your hand.

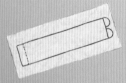

4. Add two bumps on one end for the feet, like this. Draw a dotted line a little way in from the other end.

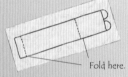

Fold here.

5. Draw another line a hand's length along, like this. Cut out the shape and fold it along the dotted lines.

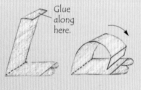

Glue along here.

6. Put some glue along the short edge, then curve the paper over. Stick the edge just behind the feet.

You could make these napkin rings for a special Easter meal.

7. Turn the head over and put two blobs of glue below the ears. Carefully, press the head onto the body.

8. To make a tail, pull a little piece off a cotton ball. Roll it into a ball, then glue it on the back of the body.

Roll up a napkin and push it through the bunny.

To bend a bunny's ear, roll it around a pencil.

Surprise eggs

1. Trim any rough edges from around a cardboard egg carton. Paint the inside with a bright paint.

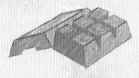

2. Turn the carton upside-down and paint the outside with the same paint. Leave the box to dry.

3. Tap the pointed end of an egg with a spoon, to crack the shell. Pull off the pieces of broken shell and tip out the inside.

4. Wash the empty shell under cold water, then leave it upside-down to dry. Crack and clean five more eggs.

5. Use crayons and food dye to decorate the eggshells. (The steps on page 48 show you how to do this.)

6. Put a tiny Easter gift, such as a small Easter egg or a toy, inside each eggshell. Put the eggs into the carton.

7. To decorate the box, fold pieces of bright cardboard. Draw half a butterfly on each piece and cut them out.

8. Close the egg box and tie a ribbon around it. Open out the butterflies and glue them onto the box.

You could hide small chocolate Easter eggs inside the eggs.

Cut flowers from wrapping paper and glue them on.

Use a felt-tip pen to add antennae to the butterflies.

You could finger print flowers all over the carton.

Glue sequins onto the carton if you like.

25

A bunch of daffodils

1. Draw a 12x12cm (5x5in.) square of bright yellow crêpe paper. Cut it out, then cut the square in half.

Tie a ribbon around the straws.

2. Make a frill all along one edge by stretching the crêpe paper gently between your fingers and thumbs.

3. Wrap the paper around the end of a wooden spoon. Slide it off a little and twist it into a point.

Snip each petal here.

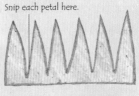

4. Fold the other piece of paper in half, short sides together. Fold it in half, then in half again. Cut it into a petal shape.

5. Open out the petals, then snip off two of the petals. Snip between each petal to separate them a little more.

6. Wrap the petals around the paper on the spoon. Wet your thumb and finger and twist the end into a point, again.

Cut out leaves from green paper.

Snip here.

7. Cut a piece off a straw, half-way down the short end. Snip the end to make two slits, like this.

8. Pull the paper off the spoon and dip the twisted end into glue. Push it into the straw and leave it to dry.

Use white crêpe paper to make narcissi. Draw along the frilled edge with an orange felt-tip pen.

9. Gently pull down each petal. Pull them a little so that they fan out evenly around the middle piece.

For a bouquet, wrap the ends of the straws in some tissue paper.

27

Easter flowerpots

Add more strips if there is room.

1. Cut two strips of masking tape and press them on either side of a terracotta pot.

2. Cut two more strips and press them onto the pot. Press the ends inside the pot, like this.

3. Cut more strips of masking tape and press them in between the other strips.

Scrunch up the paper towel.

You can wash the paint off the eraser, later.

4. Put a little acrylic paint onto a saucer. Dip a paper towel into it and dab it between the strips.

5. Fill in between all the strips of tape. Let the paint dry, then peel off the tape.

6. Put a different paint onto the saucer, then dip an eraser on the end of a pencil into it.

Cut out flowers from wrapping paper and glue them on.

28

For an Easter present, you could plant some spring flowers in your pot.

7. Press the eraser onto the pot to make the petals of a flower, like this.

8. Wash the eraser, then dip it into a different shade. Add a middle to each flower.

Chicken and egg card

1. Cut a piece of stiff paper to the length of two postcards.

2. Fold the paper in half, short sides together. Open it out.

3. Fold the short sides in, so that they meet at the middle fold.

Make the egg slightly smaller than the card.

4. Draw an egg on the back of some wrapping paper, then cut it out.

Glue the egg across the middle of the card.

5. Glue the egg on the card. Draw a zigzag from top to bottom.

Don't cut the back of the card.

6. Pull the front and back apart and cut along the zigzag.

Decorate the inside of the card with flowers.

7. Draw a chick on yellow paper. Cut it out. Add eyes and a beak.

8. Glue the chick over the fold in the middle of the card.

Use bright wrapping paper with a small pattern.

9. Draw legs with a felt-tip pen. Decorate the inside of the card.

Cress egg-heads

1. Follow steps 3 and 4 on page 24 to crack the top off an egg. Fill it with cotton balls.

2. Use a spoon to pour in water. Tip the egg so that any excess water drains out.

3. Put the egg into an egg carton. Sprinkle it with half a teaspoon of cress or mustard seeds.

4. Put the egg in a light place. Add a little water every day. The cress will grow in 7-8 days.

Overlap the ends.

5. Cut a narrow strip from the short side of a postcard. Bend it around and tape it.

6. Stand the egg on top of the cardboard. Add a face with felt-tip pens and paper.

Cut out ears and glue them on for an Easter bunny.

Add a beak and wings for a chick.

Easter recipes

Chirpy chick cupcakes

To make 6-8 cupcakes, you will need:

6 tablespoons self-rising flour
1 medium egg
¼ cup sugar
4 tablespoons margarine, softened
paper baking cups
a muffin tray
round candies and gumdrops or other candy

For the lemon butter icing:
3 tablespoons butter, softened
⅔ cup powdered sugar, sifted
1 teaspoon lemon juice (from a bottle or squeezed from a lemon)
1 drop yellow food coloring

Preheat your oven to 375°F.

The cupcakes need to be stored in an airtight container and eaten within three days.

Decorate the chicks with different-colored candies.

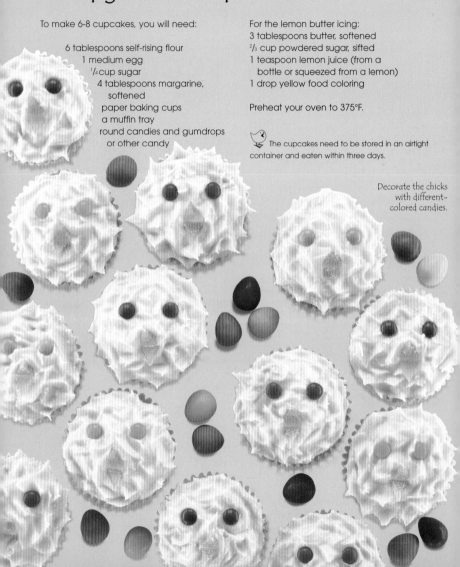

1. Pour the flour through a sifter into a bowl. Break the egg into a cup, then add it to the flour. Add the sugar and margarine.

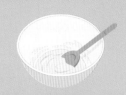

2. Beat the mixture firmly with a wooden spoon, until it is light and fluffy. Put 6-8 baking cups into pans in the muffin tray.

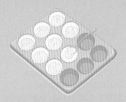

3. Using a teaspoon, half fill each baking cup with the mixture. Then, bake the cupcakes in the oven for 18-20 minutes.

Bake the cupcakes until they are golden brown.

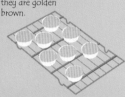

4. Take the cupcakes out of the oven. After a few minutes, lift them out of the muffin tray and put them on a rack to cool.

5. For the icing, put the butter into a bowl. Beat it with a wooden spoon until it is creamy. Stir in half of the powdered sugar.

6. Add the lemon juice, yellow food coloring and the rest of the powdered sugar. Mix everything together well.

7. Using a blunt knife, cover the top of each cupcake with butter icing. Then, use a fork to make the icing look feathery.

8. Press two round candies onto each cupcake for the eyes. Cut triangles from gumdrops or other candy for the beaks.

9. Press two triangles into the icing on each cupcake, to make a beak. Make the pointed ends stick up a little.

Flower candy

To make about 40 flowers,
you will need:

2 cups powdered sugar
1 tablespoon lemon juice
   (from a bottle or squeezed
   from a lemon)
2 teaspoons egg white, from
   dried or liquid egg white (mix
   as directed on container)
2-3 drops of lemon extract
gumdrops or other small candy
a small flower-shaped cutter
a cookie sheet

The flowers need to be stored
in an airtight container, on layers of
wax paper. Eat them within a week.

Use
non-stick
cooking spray,
if you prefer.

1. Put the cookie sheet on
a piece of wax paper.
Draw around the pan
and cut out the shape.
Put the shape in the pan.

2. Pour the powdered
sugar through a sifter into
a large bowl. Make a
hole in the middle of the
sugar with a spoon.

If the mixture is a little
dry, add a drop of water.

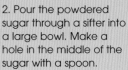

3. Mix the lemon juice, egg
white and lemon extract in
a small bowl. Pour them
into the hole in the sugar.
Stir them with a blunt knife.

4. Keep stirring everything
together until the mixture
starts to make a ball. Then,
squeeze it between your
fingers until it is smooth.

5. Sprinkle some powdered
sugar onto a clean work
surface. Sprinkle some onto
a rolling pin too, to keep
the mixture from sticking.

6. Roll out the mixture on the work surface until it is about ¼ inch thick. Then, use the cutter to cut out a flower shape.

Cut the shapes close together.

7. Put a candy onto the middle of the flower, and press it down. Then, lift the flower onto the cookie sheet with a blunt knife.

8. Cut out more flowers, one at a time, and press candy on them. If a candy won't stick, dab water on the flower, then press it on.

9. Press the scraps into a ball, roll it out again and make more flowers. Leave them on the cookie sheet for two hours, to harden.

Sticky Easter muffins

This recipe is based on cakes that are traditionally eaten in Greece at Easter.

To make 8-10 muffins, you will need:

$\frac{1}{2}$ cup soft, light brown sugar
$\frac{1}{2}$ cup (1 stick) butter, softened
2 medium eggs
2 teaspoons baking powder
1 cup flour
$\frac{1}{2}$ teaspoon ground cinnamon
$1\frac{1}{3}$ cup (4oz) finely-ground almonds*
4 tablespoons lemon juice (from a bottle or squeezed from a lemon)
muffin trays

For the orange and lemon syrup:
1 small orange
1 tablespoon lemon juice (from a bottle or squeezed from a lemon)
4 tablespoons corn syrup

Preheat your oven to 400°F.

The muffins need to be stored in an airtight container and eaten within three days. Don't pour the syrup over them more than two hours before serving.

You could serve the muffins with yogurt and fresh orange segments.

Use non-stick cooking spray, if you prefer.

1. Brush some oil inside 8-10 of the muffin holes. Cut a small circle of wax paper to put in the bottom of each.

2. Put the sugar and the butter into a large bowl. Beat them together until they are mixed well and look creamy.

* Don't give these to anyone who is allergic to nuts.

3. Break the eggs into a small bowl and beat them. Stir in the beaten eggs, a little at a time, to the creamy mixture.

4. Mix the baking powder, flour, cinnamon and almonds in a large bowl. Add them, and the lemon juice, to the mixture.

5. Mix everything well, then fill the holes in the tray $^2/_3$ full with the mixture. Bake the muffins in the oven for about 15 minutes.

The tray will still be hot.

6. Wearing oven mitts, carefully lift the muffins out of the oven. After a minute or two, loosen their sides with a blunt knife.

7. Turn the muffins onto a large plate to cool. Then, carefully peel the wax paper circles off each one.

8. For the syrup, grate some rind from about half of the orange on the fine holes on a grater. Put the rind into a small pan.

9. Cut the orange in half. Squeeze out the juice, using a lemon squeezer, and add 2 tablespoons of juice to the pan.

10. Add the lemon juice and corn syrup. Over a very low heat, gently warm the mixture, stirring it all the time.

11. When the mixture is runny, use a teaspoon to trickle it over the muffins. Let the mixture cool a little before serving.

Sunshine toast

You will need:

margarine
1 slice of bread
1 small or medium egg
a large cookie cutter
a cookie sheet

Preheat your oven to 400°F.

The toast needs to be eaten as soon as it's cooked.

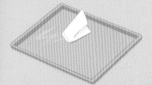

1. Dip a paper towel into some margarine. Then, rub margarine all over the cookie sheet, to grease it.

2. Using a knife, spread margarine on one side of the slice of bread. Then, press the cutter into the middle of the bread.

3. Lift out the shape you have cut out. Put both pieces of bread onto the cookie sheet, with their margarine sides upward.

You can use any cutter that makes a hole that is big enough to put an egg in.

4. Break the egg onto a saucer. Then, carefully slide the egg into the hole in the bread. Put the cookie sheet in the oven.

5. Bake the bread and egg in the oven for seven minutes, or for a little longer if you don't like a runny egg yolk.

Use a spatula.

6. Wearing oven mitts, carefully lift the cookie sheet out of the oven. Then, lift the pieces of toast onto a plate.

41

Easter truffles

To make 12 truffles, you will need:

An 8oz bar of white, milk or
   semi-sweet chocolate or
   1½ cups chocolate chips
4 tablespoons whipping cream
1 teaspoon vanilla
about 4 tablespoons sugar
   sprinkles
   paper candy cups

The truffles need to be stored in an
airtight container in the refrigerator.
Eat them within five days.

1. Pour about 1 inch of
water into a pan. Heat
the pan until the water
bubbles, then remove
the pan from the heat.

Wear
oven
mitts.

2. Put the chocolate and
cream into a heatproof
bowl. Using oven mitts,
carefully put the bowl
into the pan.

3. Stir the chocolate and
cream with a wooden
spoon until the chocolate
has melted. Carefully lift
the bowl out of the water.

4. Leave the bowl to cool for 20 minutes, then stir in the vanilla. Put the mixture in the refrigerator for 1½ hours, until it is very firm.

5. Put the sugar sprinkles onto a plate. Scoop up some chocolate mixture with a teaspoon and put it into the sugar sprinkles.

6. Using your fingers, roll the spoonful in the sprinkles to make a ball. When it is covered, put it in a candy cup. Make more truffles.

7. Put the truffles onto a plate, then put them in the refrigerator for 30 minutes, until they are hard. Keep them in the refrigerator.

To make truffle eggs, squash the spoonful of mixture slightly when you roll it in the sugar sprinkles.

Marzipan animals and eggs

To make 4 chicks, 3 rabbits and lots of eggs and carrots, you will need:

9oz pack of marzipan*
yellow and red food coloring
toothpicks

The animals and eggs need to be stored in an airtight container and eaten within three weeks.

Chicks

Wrap one half in plastic foodwrap.

1. Unwrap the marzipan and cut it in half. Put one half in a small bowl and add 12 drops of yellow food coloring.

2. Mix the coloring in with your fingers until the marzipan is completely yellow. Then, cut the piece of marzipan in half.

3. Put one half in a bowl and mix in a drop of red coloring. If the marzipan isn't bright orange, add another drop of red.

Keep this piece for the wings.

4. Cut the yellow marzipan into five pieces. Make four of them into balls. Then, squeeze them at one end to make tear shapes.

5. Make eight small yellow wings and press two onto each body. Then, roll a beak from orange marzipan and press it on.

Press in two eyes with a toothpick.

6. For the feet, make a tiny orange ball and flatten it. Cut the shape halfway across and open it out. Press a chick on top.

* Marzipan contains ground nuts, so don't give these to anyone who is allergic to nuts.

Rabbits

Use plastic foodwrap.

1. Unwrap the plain marzipan. Mix one drop of red coloring into it to make pink. Cut it in half and wrap one half.

2. Cut the unwrapped piece in half. With one half, make three balls for the bodies. Then, cut the other piece in half.

3. From one half, roll three smaller balls, for the heads. Then, make six ears, three tails and three noses from the other half.

If the ears won't stick, dip the ends in water.

4. Pinch each ear to make a fold. Press ears, a head, nose and tail onto each body. Then, press in eyes with a toothpick.

Marbled eggs

1. Unwrap the second piece of pink marzipan. Add a drop of red coloring, and start to mix it in with your hands.

2. Stop mixing in the coloring when the marzipan looks marbled. Roll the marzipan into lots of little egg shapes.

Use orange marzipan to make carrots. Make marks on them with a blunt knife.

Press a rabbit's head on the front of its body, to make it look as if it is lying down.

Easter fudge

To make 36 pieces of fudge, you will need:

1lb box of powdered sugar
about 16 (4oz) jumbo marshmallows
2 tablespoons milk
1/2 cup (1 stick) unsalted butter
1/2 teaspoon vanilla
2 drops yellow food coloring
a shallow cake pan

Find out how to wrap your fudge like this on page 62.

 The fudge needs to be stored in an airtight container in the refrigerator and eaten within a week.

Use non-stick cooking spray, if you prefer.

1. Put the pan onto a piece of wax paper. Using a pencil, draw around the pan and cut out the square.

2. Using a paper towel, wipe some oil onto the sides and bottom of the pan. Press in the paper square and wipe it too.

3. Pour the powdered sugar through a sifter into a large bowl. Make a small hollow in the middle of the sugar with a spoon.

Use a spoon.

4. Using clean scissors, cut the marshmallows in half and put them in a small pan. Add the milk, butter and vanilla.

5. Gently heat the pan. Stir the mixture every now and then with a wooden spoon until everything has melted.

6. Pour the mixture into the hollow in the sugar. Beat everything together until it is smooth, then mix in the food coloring.

Smooth the top with
the back of
a spoon.

7. Put the fudge into the
pan and push it into the
corners. When it is cool,
put it in the refrigerator for
three hours to harden.

To make
pink fudge,
use pink
marshmallows
and add a
drop of red
or pink food
coloring.

8. Loosen the edges of
the fudge with a blunt
knife, then turn it out
onto a cutting board.
Remove the paper.

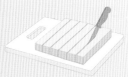

9. Cut the fudge into 36
pieces. Put the pieces in
an airtight container in
the refrigerator for an
hour to harden.

Colored eggs

To make six colored eggs, you will need:

6 eggs, at room temperature
food coloring
wax crayons
tiny star-shaped stickers
rubber bands

The eggs need to be stored in a refrigerator and eaten within three days. They can be eaten with a fresh mixed salad or on their own.

Cooking the eggs

Use a slotted spoon.

1. Put the eggs into a pan of cold water. Heat the pan until the water is gently boiling, then reduce the heat a little.

2. Cook the eggs for eight to nine minutes. Lift out one egg at a time. Cool them in a bowl of cold water for ten minutes.

Wax patterns

The wax resists the food coloring.

Leave the egg for about ten minutes.

1. Using a wax crayon, draw patterns on a dry egg. Then, put 3-4 teaspoons of bright food coloring into a glass.

2. Half fill the glass with water, then put the egg into the glass. Using a spoon, turn the egg to color it all over.

3. When the egg is brightly colored, lift it out of the glass with a spoon. Put the egg on a paper towel to dry.

Stickers

Make sure the egg is dry.

1. Press tiny stickers onto an egg. Use shiny ones if you can, because they don't soak up so much food coloring.

2. Color the egg in a glass, as you did before. Then, lift the egg out with a spoon and put it on a paper towel to dry.

3. When the coloring is dry, peel off the stickers. You'll see the color of the eggshell where the stickers were.

These rabbits and chicks were painted straight onto the eggs with food coloring.

Stripes

1. Stretch a short, thick rubber band around a dry egg. Then, stretch one around the egg from the top to the bottom.

2. Add lots more rubber bands, then color the egg and let it dry. Then, remove the rubber bands to see stripes of eggshell.

49

Easter cake

You will need:

1⅔ cups self-rising flour
1 teaspoon baking powder
4 medium eggs
1 cup and 2 tablespoons sugar
1 cup (2 sticks) margarine,
    softened
two round cake pans

For the butter icing:
2 cups powdered sugar
½ cup (1 stick) unsalted butter,
    softened
1 tablespoon milk
1 teaspoon vanilla

Preheat your oven to 350°F.

The cake needs to be stored in an airtight container in a cool place and eaten within three days.

To make the icing yellow, add a teaspoon of yellow food coloring at step 8.

Decorate the cake with flower candies (pages 36-37) and marzipan chicks (pages 44-45).

50

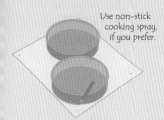

Use non-stick cooking spray, if you prefer.

1. Put the cake pans onto a piece of wax paper and draw around them. Cut out the circles, just inside the line.

2. Wipe the sides and bottoms of the pans with a little oil. Put the paper circles inside and wipe them with a little oil too.

3. Using a sifter, sift the flour and baking powder into a large bowl. Then, carefully break the eggs into a cup.

Be careful – the cakes will be hot.

4. Add the eggs, sugar and margarine to the bowl. Beat everything with a wooden spoon until they are mixed well.

5. Put half of the mixture into each pan. Smooth the tops with the back of a spoon. Then, bake the cakes for 25 minutes.

6. Press the cakes with a finger. If they are cooked, they will spring back. Let them cool a little, then put them on a wire rack.

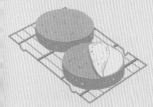

7. Peel the paper off the cakes and leave them to cool. When the cakes are cold, sift the powdered sugar into a bowl.

8. Add the butter, milk and vanilla. Stir the ingredients together, then beat them until the mixture is fluffy. Put one cake on a plate.

9. Spread the cake with half of the icing. Then, put the other cake on top and spread it with the rest of the icing.

Chocolate nests

To make 10 nests, you will need:

an 8oz chocolate bar or 1½ cups
   chocolate chips
¼ cup (½ stick) butter
2 tablespoons corn syrup
4 cups cornflakes
30 chocolate mini eggs or jellybeans
paper baking cups
muffin trays

The nests need to be stored in an
airtight container in the refrigerator.
Eat them within three days.

1. Put ten baking cups
into pans in the muffin
tray. Break the chocolate
into squares and put
them in a large pan.

52

The syrup slides off the hot spoon.

Try not to crush the flakes.

2. Add the butter to the pan. Dip a tablespoon in some hot water, then use the spoon to add the corn syrup.

3. Heat the pan gently, stirring the ingredients all the time, until the butter and chocolate have completely melted.

4. Turn off the heat, then add the cornflakes to the pan. Gently stir them into the chocolate, until they are coated all over.

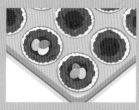

Push the flakes up the sides.

5. Fill the baking cups with the mixture. Using the back of a teaspoon, make a hollow in the middle of each nest.

6. Arrange three mini eggs in each nest. Then, put the tray in the refrigerator and leave it for about an hour to set.

7. Take the nests out of the baking cups and put them on a plate. Keep them in the refrigerator until you want to eat them.

Easter fruit bread

To make a loaf with about 12 slices, you will need:

2 cups (8oz) bread flour
$\frac{1}{2}$ teaspoon ground all-spice
$\frac{1}{2}$ teaspoon salt
2 tablespoons butter
1 tablespoon sugar
2 teaspoons rapid-rise dried yeast
1 medium egg and 5 tablespoons milk, beaten together
$\frac{2}{3}$ cup (4oz) dried mixed fruit, chopped into bite-sized pieces
a little milk for brushing
a 8 x 5 x $3\frac{1}{2}$in loaf pan

For the icing:
$\frac{1}{2}$ cup powdered sugar
1 tablespoon lemon juice (from a bottle or squeezed from a lemon)
$\frac{1}{4}$ cup ($1\frac{1}{2}$oz) chopped Maraschino cherries

Preheat your oven to 400°F.

Easter fruit bread needs to be stored in an airtight container and eaten within three days.

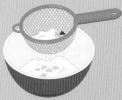

Use non-stick cooking spray, if you prefer.

1. Put the pan onto wax paper. Draw around it and cut out the shape. Grease the pan and put the paper in the bottom.

2. Pour the flour, all-spice and salt through a sifter into a large bowl. Cut the butter into cubes and add it to the bowl.

3. Using your fingertips, rub in the butter until the mixture looks like breadcrumbs. Stir in the sugar and yeast.

54

If the mixture is too dry, add 1 tablespoon of milk.

Continue until the dough is smooth and springy.

4. Pour the egg mixture into the bowl. Then, stir everything with a wooden spoon until you make a stiff dough.

5. Sprinkle some flour onto a clean, dry work surface. Then, knead the dough by pushing it away from you with both hands.

6. Fold the dough in half and turn it around. Push it away again. Do this for five minutes, then put it into a greased bowl.

Knead in the fruit for a couple of minutes.

7. Cover the bowl with plastic foodwrap. Leave it in a warm place for an hour, until the dough has risen to twice its size.

8. Turn the dough out of the bowl and sprinkle the dried fruit over it. Knead the fruit into the dough until it is mixed in.

9. Put the dough in the pan and cover the pan with plastic foodwrap. Put it in a warm place for about 45 minutes to rise some more.

Remove the wax paper.

Use a teaspoon to drizzle the icing onto the loaf.

10. Turn on your oven. Brush the top of the dough with milk, then put the pan in the oven and bake the bread for 30-35 minutes.

11. Push a skewer into the loaf. If it comes out clean, the loaf is cooked. Take the loaf out of the pan. Put it on a wire rack to cool.

12. Sift the powdered sugar into a bowl and mix in the lemon juice. Drizzle the icing over the loaf, then scatter the cherries on top.

Spiced Easter cookies

To make about 25 cookies, you will need:

1 medium egg
½ cup (1 stick) butter, softened
6 tablespoons sugar
1½ cups all-purpose flour
½ teaspoon cinnamon
½ teaspoon ginger
½ cup dried cranberries or
   raisins cut in half
5 teaspoons milk

about 2 tablespoons sugar
a 2½in fluted cookie cutter
two greased cookie sheets

Preheat your oven to 400°F.

The cookies need to be stored in an airtight container and eaten within five days.

1. Carefully break the egg on the edge of a small bowl, and pour it slowly onto a saucer. Then, put a egg cup over the yolk.

You will use the egg white later.

2. Hold the cup over the yolk and tip the saucer over the small bowl, so that the egg white dribbles into it.

Use a wooden spoon.

3. Put the butter and sugar into a large bowl and beat them until they are creamy. Then, add the egg yolk and beat it in.

Find out how to make cellophane bags for your cookies on page 63.

4. Using a sifter, sift the flour, cinnamon and ginger into the bowl. Then, add the cranberries (or raisins) and the milk too.

5. Mix everything together with a spoon, then squeeze the mixture with your hands until you have made a dough.

6. Wrap the dough in plastic foodwrap. Put it in the refrigerator for 20 minutes. Sprinkle a clean work surface with flour.

Sprinkle flour on a rolling pin.

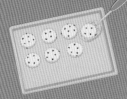

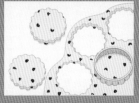

7. Turn on your oven. Then, put the dough onto the work surface. Roll the dough out until it is about 1/4 inch thick.

8. Use the cutter to cut out lots of cookies. Then, carefully lift the cookies onto the cookie sheets, using a spatula.

9. Squeeze the scraps of dough together to make a ball. Then, roll the dough out as you did before and cut out more cookies.

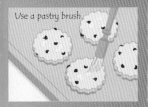

Use a pastry brush.

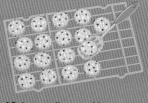

10. Using a fork, beat the egg white for a few seconds until it is frothy. Brush a little egg white on the top of each cookie.

11. Sprinkle a little sugar over each cookie. Bake them in the oven for 12-15 minutes. They will turn golden brown.

12. Leave the cookies on the cookie sheets for about five minutes. Then, lift them onto a wire rack and leave them to cool.

Easter daisy cookies

To make about 50 cookies, you will need:

³/₄ cup powdered sugar
10 tablespoons butter, softened
a lemon
2 cups all-purpose flour
writing icing or gel
gum drops or other candies for decorating
a flower-shaped cookie cutter
two greased cookie sheets

Heat your oven to 350°F.

The cookies need to be stored in an airtight container and eaten within three days.

Use a sifter.

1. Sift the powdered sugar into a large bowl. Add the butter and mix everything together with a spoon until the mixture is creamy.

2. Grate the rind from the lemon using the medium holes on a grater. Then, add the rind to the bowl and mix everything again.

Use a lemon squeezer.

Sprinkle some flour on a rolling pin too.

3. Cut the lemon in half and squeeze the juice from it. Then, stir a tablespoon of lemon juice into the creamy mixture.

4. Pour the flour through a sifter into the bowl. Mix it in until you make a smooth dough. Then, wrap the dough in plastic foodwrap.

5. Put the dough in a refrigerator for 30 minutes, to become firmer. Then, sprinkle some flour onto a clean work surface.

6. Turn on your oven. Then, roll out the dough until it is about $\frac{1}{4}$ inch thick. Cut out lots of flower shapes, using the cutter.

This recipe makes 50 cookies this size. The number of cookies depends on the size of your cutter.

7. Put the flower shapes onto the greased sheets. Squeeze the scraps into a ball, then roll it out again and cut out more shapes.

The cookies should be lightly browned.

8. Bake the cookies for 15 minutes. Leave them on the cookie sheets for two minutes, then put them on a wire rack to cool.

9. When the cookies are cool, decorate them with icing. Draw lines, swirls and dots. Press candy into the middle of the icing.

Cheesy chicks

To make about 15 chicks, you will need:

3oz sharp cheddar cheese
1 cup all-purpose flour
$^1/_4$ cup ($^1/_2$ stick) butter, refrigerated
the yolk from a medium egg
4 teaspoons cold water
a chick-shaped or other cookie cutter
two greased cookie sheets

Preheat your oven to 375°F.

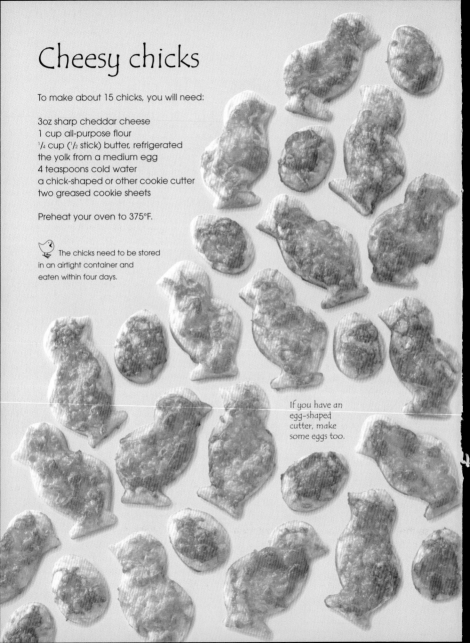 The chicks need to be stored
in an airtight container and
eaten within four days.

If you have an
egg-shaped
cutter, make
some eggs too.

Use the fine holes on a grater.

1. Grate the cheese. Sift the flour through a sifter into a large bowl. Then, cut the butter into chunks and add it to the bowl.

2. Mix in the butter until it is coated in flour. Rub it in with your fingers, until it looks like breadcrumbs. Add half of the cheese.

3. Mix the egg yolk and water in a small bowl. Put two teaspoonfuls in a cup, then pour the rest over the flour mixture.

4. Stir everything together, then squeeze the mixture until you make a smooth dough. Make it a slightly flattened round shape.

5. Wrap the dough in plastic foodwrap and put it in the refrigerator for 30 minutes. While it is in there, turn on your oven.

6. Sprinkle flour onto a clean work surface and a rolling pin. Then, roll out the dough until it is about $1/4$ inch thick.

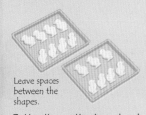

Leave spaces between the shapes.

7. Use the cutter to cut out chick shapes. Put them onto the cookie sheets. Squeeze the scraps into a ball, then roll them out.

8. Cut out more shapes. Brush the tops of the shapes with the egg mixture, then sprinkle them with grated cheese.

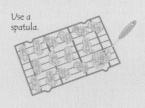

Use a spatula.

9. Bake the chicks for 12 minutes. Leave them on the cookie sheets for five minutes, then put them on a wire rack to cool.

Boxes and bags

Bunny boxes

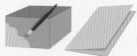

This side of the head needs to be on the fold.

1. Carefully cut the top off a tissue box and paint the box. Find a piece of thick paper the same color. Fold the paper in half.

2. Draw half of a bunny's head, like this. Keeping the paper folded, cut out the shape. Open out the paper and flatten it.

3. Draw a face. Then, glue the head onto one end of the box. Glue a large cotton ball onto the opposite end, for a tail.

Pretty candy

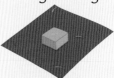

Pile candy or cookies into a bunny box as an Easter gift.

1. Cut a square of thin cellophane that is bigger than the candy, like this. Then, put the candy in the middle of the square.

2. Wrap the cellophane around the candy and tape it. Tie a piece of ribbon around each end of the candy.

Candy bags

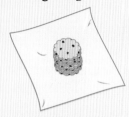

Leave long ends on the ribbon.

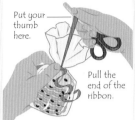

Put your thumb here.

Pull the end of the ribbon.

1. Carefully cut a square of thin cellophane. Then, place several cookies or candy in the middle of the square.

2. Gather up the edges of the square and tie a piece of ribbon around the cellophane, above the cookies.

3. To make the ribbon curl, hold it between your thumb and the blade of some closed scissors, and pull it firmly.

Add a paper handle to a box to make a basket.

Save food boxes and wrap ribbons around them.

Easter tags

1. Draw a rectangle on a piece of white cardboard with a wax crayon. Then, draw the body of a chick with a yellow crayon.

2. Add a beak, a leg and an eye. Paint over the picture with runny paint. The crayon lines will show through the paint.

3. When the paint is dry, cut around the rectangle, leaving a painted edge. Tape a piece of ribbon to the back of the tag.

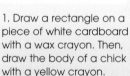

Draw an egg shape and fill it with lines and patterns.

You can fill different areas with different colors of paint, like this flower.